Busy Lizzie

Written by Lisa Thompson
Pictures by Craig Smith

Lizzie wanted to be a pirate.

"If you want to work hard, come on board," said the Captain.

On Monday, Lizzie had to mop the decks.
She was busy all day.

"This work is not too hard," she said.
"The life of a pirate is the life for me."

On Tuesday, Lizzie spent all day peeling potatoes.

"What a big pile of potatoes! Pirates must get very hungry," said Lizzie.

Lizzie was busy on Wednesday.
She had to mend all the sails.

"Keep working, Lizzie! There are lots
more sails to mend," said Fingers, the parrot.

On Thursday, busy Lizzie had to sail the ship.

"Look out, Lizzie!" shouted the crew.
"Keep away from the rocks!"

The next day was Friday.
The Captain sent Lizzie to hunt for treasure.
She hunted all day on an island.

"The life of a pirate is the life for me," she said.

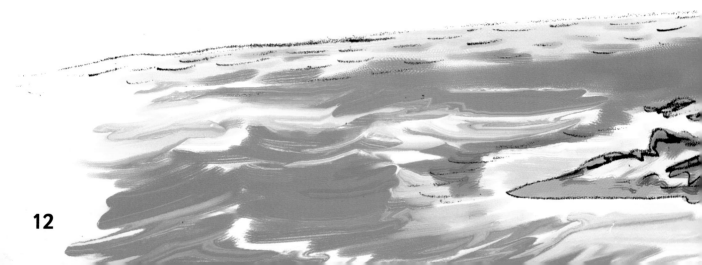

On Saturday, Lizzie was still busy looking for treasure. She dug a big hole in the sand.

"This *is* hard work," said Lizzie.
"I hope pirates get a day off on Sunday!"